level 3

THEORY LESSONS

by JAMES BASTIEN

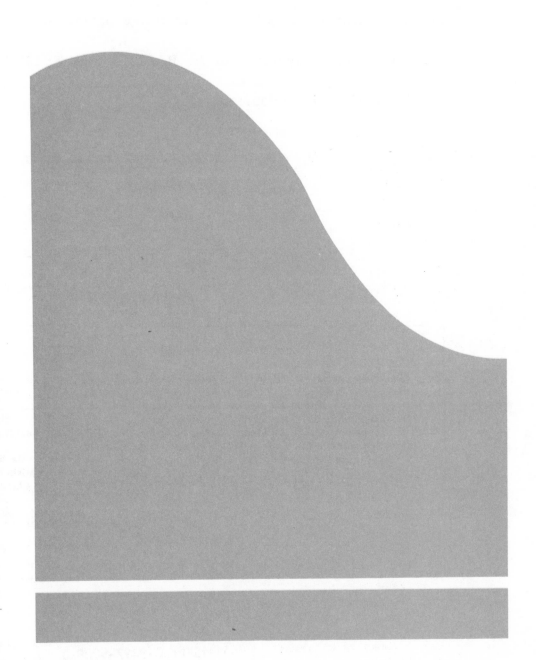

KJOS WEST · Neil A. Kjos, Jr. Publisher · San Diego, California

PREFACE

THEORY LESSONS is designed to be used simultaneously with PIANO LESSONS by level. The written and playing exercises reinforce concepts presented in PIANO LESSONS.

THEORY LESSONS may be used for either private or class instruction. Although the materials are correlated with the BASTIEN PIANO LIBRARY, the series may be used with any other piano course.

Suggested Use of Materials with "PIANO LESSONS, Level 3."

After completing **page 5**, the student is ready to begin . . . .**Theory Lessons**-Level 3 (WP9)
After completing **page 9**, the student is ready to begin . . . . **Technic Lessons**-Level 3 (WP14)
After completing **page 11**, the student is ready to begin . . . . **Piano Solos**-Level 3 (WP25)
After completing **page 15**, the student is ready to begin . . . .**Sight Reading**-Level 3 (WP18)
After completing **page 17**, the student is ready to begin . . . . **First Hanon Studies**-Level 3 (WP31)
After completing **page 22**, the student is ready to begin
these Supplementary Books . . . .**Bastien Favorites**-Level 3 (GP84)
Christmas Favorites-Level 3 (WP48)
Christmas Duets-Level 3 (GP313)
Duet Favorites-Level 3 (WP62)
Favorite Classic Melodies-Level 3 (WP75)
First Piano Repertoire Album-Level 3-4 (WP70)
First Sonatinas (GP302)
Pop Piano Styles-Level 3 (WP53)

SHEET MUSIC from **Level Three Solos** may be assigned to the student at the teacher's discretion.

8/81

ISBN 0-8497-5008-3

CONTENTS

Major Sharp Key Signatures 4
Writing Major Sharp Key Signatures 5
Accompaniment Styles 6
Question and Answer Phrases 8
Sight Reading Phrases 9
Intervals of the Scale 10
Triads of the Scale 11
Leger Line and Space Notes 12
Triplets 13
Question and Answer Phrases 14
Relative Minor Scales 15
Forms of Minor Scales 16
Minor Key Signatures 18
Major-Minor Triads 19
Triads and Inversions 20
Recognizing Inverted Triads 21
Major Flat Key Signatures 22
Writing Major Flat Key Signatures 23
Music Signs 24
The Group 3 Keys (Db, Ab, Eb) 25
Db Major Scale 26
Primary Chords in Db Major 27
Ab Major Scale 28
Primary Chords in Ab Major 29
Eb Major Scale 30
Primary Chords in Eb Major 31
Circle of Keys 32
Key Signature Review 33
Leger Line and Space Note Review 34
Final Review (Level 3) 35
Manuscript Paper 38

Major Sharp Key Signatures

1. The sharps are <u>always</u> written in this order on the staff.

Write the order of sharps three times on this staff.

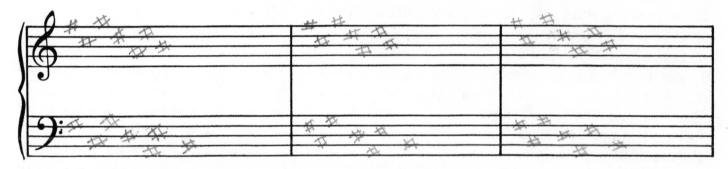

2. To find the Major key name of a piece with sharps in the signature:

   1. Name the <u>last</u> sharp to the right. (The last sharp is the <u>seventh</u> tone of the Major scale.)

   2. Name the next letter in the musical alphabet (go up a half step). This is the name of the Major key.

   Examples:

   D Major   B Major   F# Major

Name these Major key signatures.

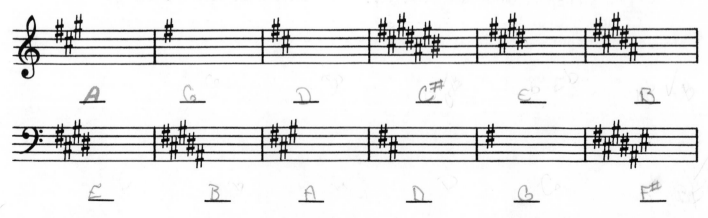

* *TEACHER: Have the student drill on the sharp key signatures using his BASTIEN "<u>MUSIC FLASHCARDS</u>."*

Writing Major Sharp Key Signatures

3. To write the Major sharp key signatures:

Write the sharps in their order until you
write the sharp <u>before</u> the key note.

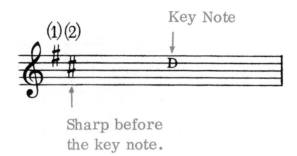

Write these Major key signatures.

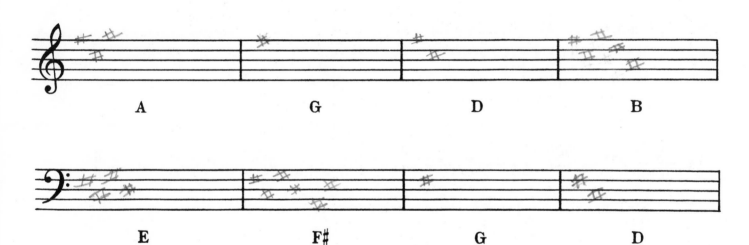

A   G   D   B

E   F♯   G   D

4. Write these Major key signatures in both clefs.

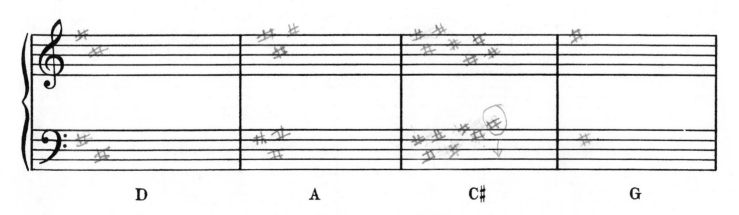

D   A   C♯   G

Accompaniment Styles

5. Various kinds of bass accompaniment styles can be used to harmonize melodies.

The "WESTERN BASS" uses the first, fifth and sixth degrees of the scale.

Scale Degrees: 1 5 6 5

Write this bass pattern for measures 2 through 5. Play this piece.

Key of _____   Transpose: C, F

5 2 1

6. Notes of chords may be played together to form block chords. Notes of chords may also be played broken (not played at the same time).

There are many kinds of BROKEN CHORD BASS patterns. Here is one kind in which the notes of the chords are played one-at-a-time.

Write this bass pattern for measures 2 through 7. Play this piece.

Key of _____   Transpose: G, F, D, A, E

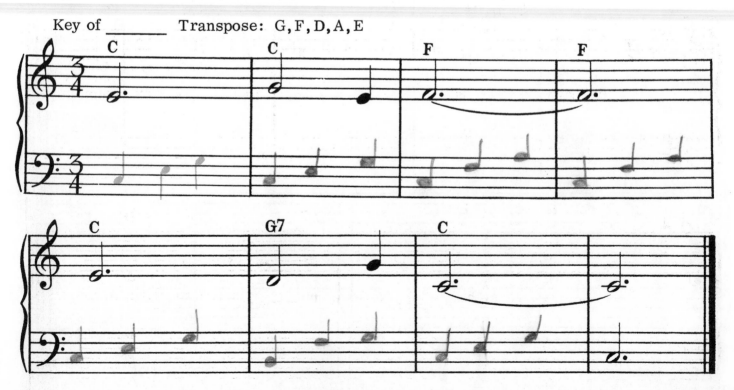

7. Here is another BROKEN CHORD BASS pattern.

Write this bass pattern for measures 2 through 7.   Play this piece.

Key of _____   Transpose: C, G, D, A, E

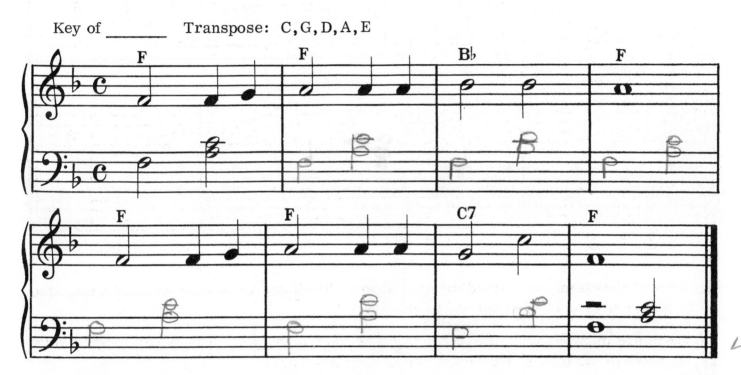

8. Using the same style broken bass shown in number 7, write the bass part for the blank measures in "Home, Sweet Home." Play this piece.

HOME SWEET HOME

Key of _____   Transpose: C, F

Through | man - sions and | pal - a - ces | though _ we may | roam, Be it

ev - er so | hum - ble, there's | no _____ place like | home.

WP 9

Question and Answer Phrases

Make up (improvise) answer phrases to these question phrases. Write your best "answers" on the staffs.

Write both melody and harmony to complete these lines.

Sight Reading Phrases

Write the key name for each piece below. Write in your own dynamics. Play and count aloud. Keep your eyes on the music while playing.

14. Key of _____ Transpose: C, G

15. Key of _____

16. Key of _____ Transpose: D

17. Key of _____ Transpose: A, D

WP 9

Intervals of the Scale

18. The intervals of the C Major scale are shown below. Notice that the 2nd, 3rd, 6th and 7th intervals are called <u>Major</u> intervals. The 4th, 5th and 8th intervals are called <u>Perfect</u> intervals. These intervals are the same for all Major scales. Play each interval, listening carefully to the sound.

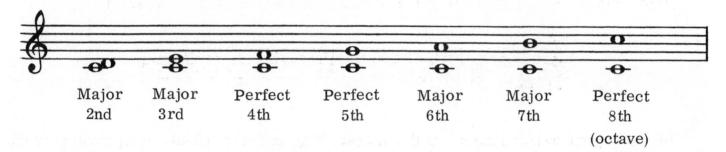

| Major
2nd | Major
3rd | Perfect
4th | Perfect
5th | Major
6th | Major
7th | Perfect
8th
(octave) |

19. Two notes played together form a <u>harmonic</u> interval. Name these harmonic intervals of the G Major scale. Write <u>M</u> for Major, <u>P</u> for Perfect and write <u>2</u> for 2nd, <u>3</u> for 3rd, etc. Play these intervals.

M2 ___ ___ ___ ___ ___ ___

20. Two notes played separately form a <u>melodic</u> interval. Name these melodic intervals of the F Major scale. Play them.

M3 ___ ___ ___ ___ ___ ___

21. Draw an upper note to complete these harmonic intervals of the D Major scale. Play them.

| Major
2nd | Major
3rd | Perfect
4th | Perfect
5th | Major
6th | Major
7th | Perfect
8th
(octave) |

22. Name these intervals. Think of the scale to which each interval belongs. Play them.

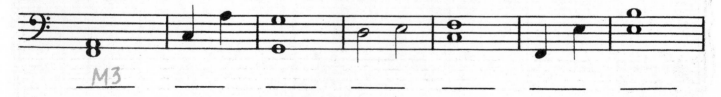

M3 ___ ___ ___ ___ ___ ___

Triads of the Scale

23. A triad is a 3-note chord. In root position the notes are either all line notes or all space notes 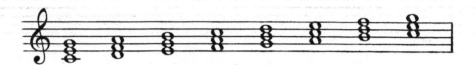 .

Here are the triads of the C Major scale. Play them forward and backward. Play first with the R.H., then with the L.H. Transpose to the keys of G and F.

24. Write in your own dynamics for this piece. Play and count aloud. Keep your eyes on the music while playing.

25. Make up (improvise) several melodies using triads of the scale. Write your best composition on this staff. Write in your own dynamics.

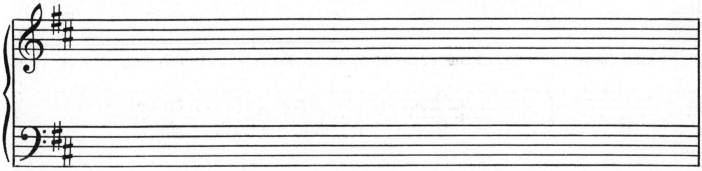

26. Write the triads of the D Major scale in both clefs. Play these triads.

Leger Line and Space Notes

27. The short lines added above or below the staff are called <u>leger lines</u>. Line and space notes are written on these short leger lines.

   Leger line and space notes between the staffs are played near the <u>middle</u> of the piano. Play these inner leger line and space notes.

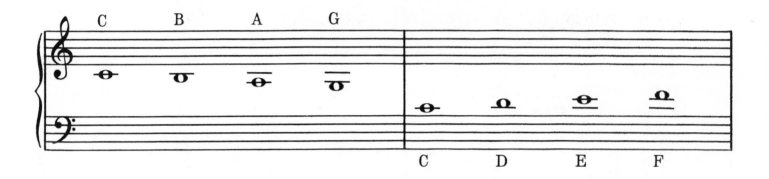

28. Name these notes. The letter names spell words. Play them.

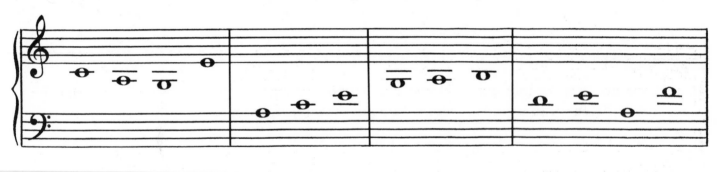

29. Leger line and space notes above the Treble Clef are played <u>high</u> on the piano. Leger line and space notes below the Bass Clef are played <u>low</u> on the piano.

   Play these upper and lower leger line and space notes.

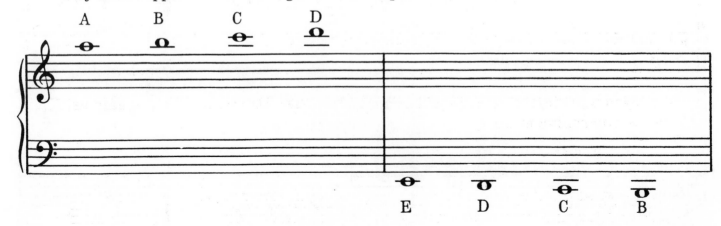

30. Name these notes. The letter names spell words. Play them.

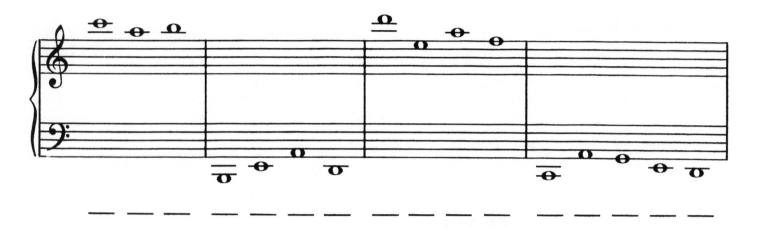

Triplets

The word triplet means <u>three</u>. A triplet figure is usually indicated by a *3* and a slur.

A triplet eighth note figure is equal to one quarter note.

31. First, clap and count the rhythm of these melodies. Next, play and count them.

a.

b.

32. Write two measures to complete this melody. Use some triplets.

WP 9

Question and Answer Phrases

Make up (improvise) answer phrases to these question phrases. Write your best "answers" on the staffs.

33.

34.

35.

Write a melody and the harmony indicated by the chord symbols to complete these lines.

36.

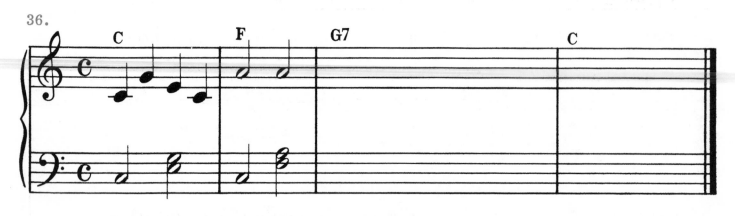

37.

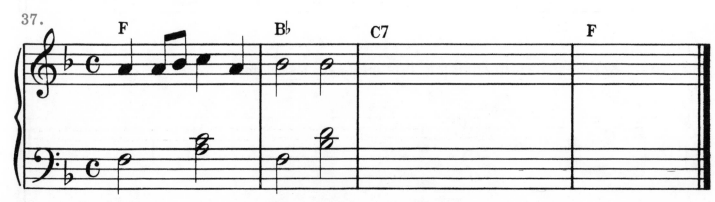

Relative Minor Scales

Every Major scale has a <u>relative</u> <u>minor</u> <u>scale.</u>   Both scales have the <u>same</u> key signature.

The relative minor scale begins on the <u>sixth</u> tone (degree) of the Major scale.

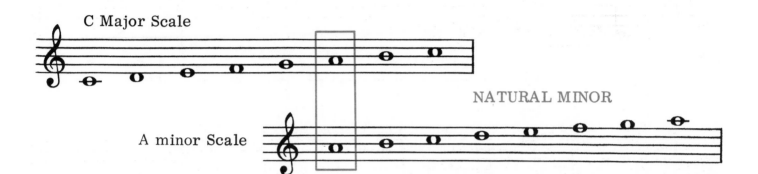

38.   Write the D Natural minor scale.   It is the relative minor scale of F Major. (Both scales have the same key signature.)

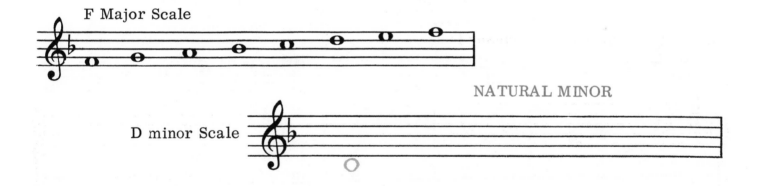

39. Write the E Natural minor scale. It is the relative minor scale of G Major.

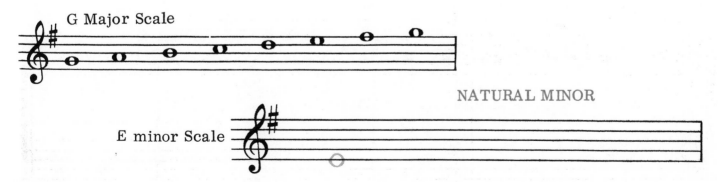

Forms of Minor Scales

Each Major scale has only <u>one</u> form.   Each minor scale has <u>three</u> forms:

(1) NATURAL   (2) HARMONIC   (3) MELODIC

NATURAL MINOR ——— The notes are the <u>same</u> as the relative Major.

HARMONIC MINOR ——— The <u>7th tone</u> (degree) is <u>raised a half step</u>. The raised 7th must be written in as an accidental, because it is not in the key signature.

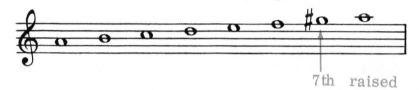

7th raised

MELODIC MINOR ——— The <u>6th</u> and <u>7th tones</u> are <u>raised a half step going up,</u> then <u>lowered going down.</u>   The scale going down is exactly the same as the Natural minor scale.

6th   7th raised   7th   6th lowered

40.   Write the Harmonic and Melodic forms of the D minor scale. Play all these scales.

NATURAL

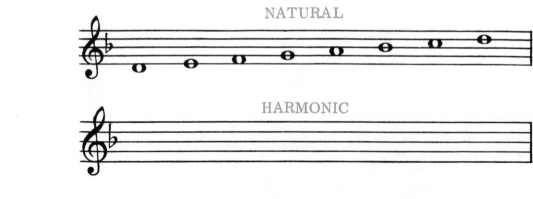

HARMONIC

MELODIC

41. Write the Harmonic and Melodic forms of the E minor scale. Play all three scales.

NATURAL

HARMONIC

MELODIC

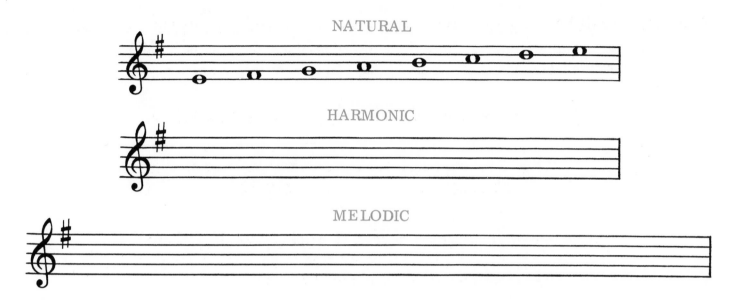

42. Change these Natural Minor scales to <u>Harmonic Minor</u> scales by writing a sharp in the correct place. Play these scales.

B minor

G minor

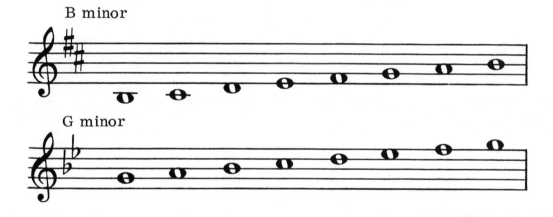

43. Change these Natural Minor scales to <u>Melodic Minor</u> scales by writing in the correct accidentals. Play these scales.

B minor

G minor

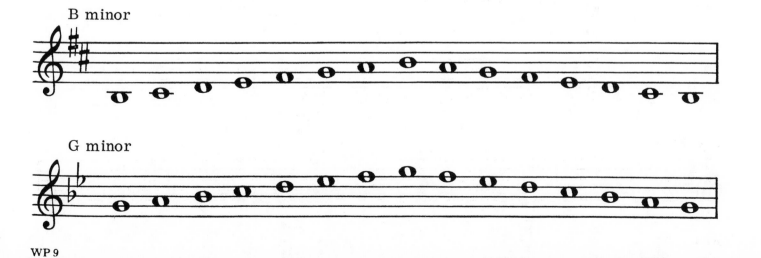

Minor Key Signatures

Both the relative Major and its relative minor key have the <u>same</u> signature. To tell wheth-
er a piece is in Major or minor, look at the first and last notes. These are <u>clues</u> which
help tell Major or minor. Also, listen to see if the piece sounds Major or minor. If the
piece sounds minor, you can find the minor key name with this rule:

Count <u>down three half steps</u> from the Major key name.

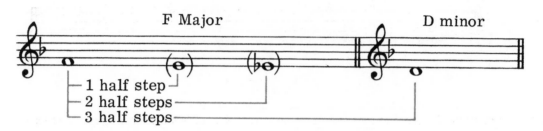

44. Write the minor key name on the blanks.

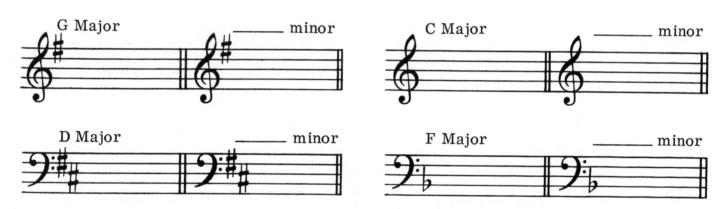

45. Look at the first and last notes in each melody. Play each melody and listen to the
sound. Write the Major or minor key name on the blanks.

Major - Minor Triads

To write a minor triad, <u>lower</u> the <u>middle note</u> of a Major triad <u>one half step.</u>

46. First, write the Major triad as indicated. Next, write the minor triad. Play these chords.

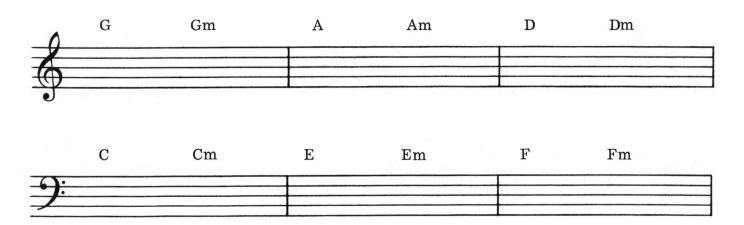

47. Name and play these Major and minor triads.

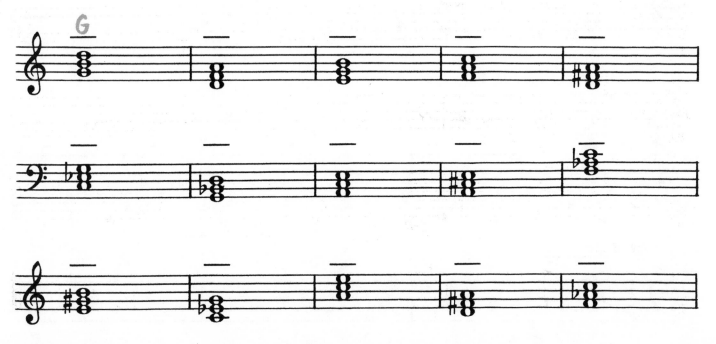

Triads and Inversions

The note on which a triad is built is called the ROOT. A triad in ROOT position has notes which are either on all lines 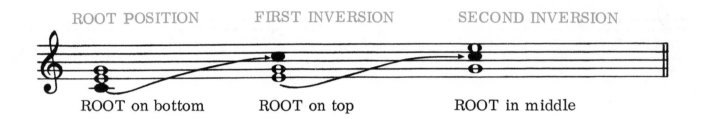 or all spaces .

Any ROOT position triad may be INVERTED (rearranged) by moving the <u>root note</u> to the <u>top</u> or <u>middle</u>.

ROOT POSITION   FIRST INVERSION   SECOND INVERSION

ROOT on bottom   ROOT on top   ROOT in middle

Write the inversions of these triads. Play all three chords in each key.

ROOT POSITION   FIRST INVERSION   SECOND INVERSION

48. G Major

49. A minor

50. F Major

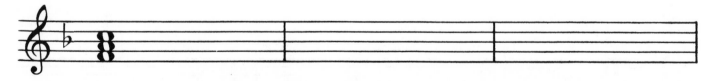

51. D minor

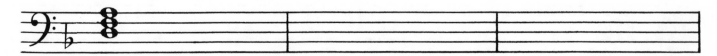

Recognizing Inverted Triads

FIRST INVERSION TRIADS have two notes at the bottom close
together (to form an interval of a <u>third</u>).

The ROOT is always the <u>top</u> note of the interval of the <u>fourth</u>.

52. Find the <u>first inversion</u> triads in this group. Circle the <u>root</u> and write the root name
of each first inversion triad. Play these chords.

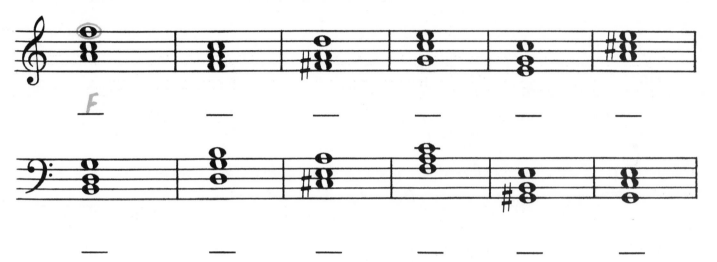

SECOND INVERSION TRIADS have two notes at the top close
together (to form an interval of a <u>third</u>).

The ROOT is always the <u>top</u> note of the interval of the <u>fourth</u>.

53. Find the <u>second inversion</u> triads in this group. Circle the <u>root</u> and write the root name
of each second inversion triad. Play these chords.

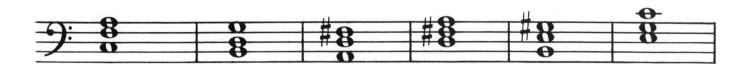

WP 9

Major Flat Key Signatures

54. The flats are <u>always</u> written in this order on the staff.

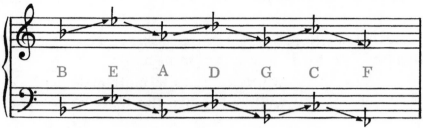

Write the order of flats three times on this staff.

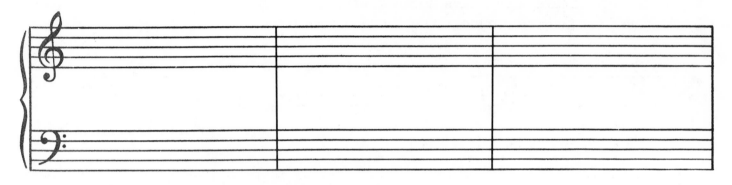

55. To find the Major key name of a piece with flats in the signature:

1. Look at the <u>next-to-the-last</u> flat.

2. The letter name of this flat is the name of the Major key. *

Bb Major

EXCEPTIONS

F Major (one flat)   C Major (no sharps or flats)

Name these Major key signatures.

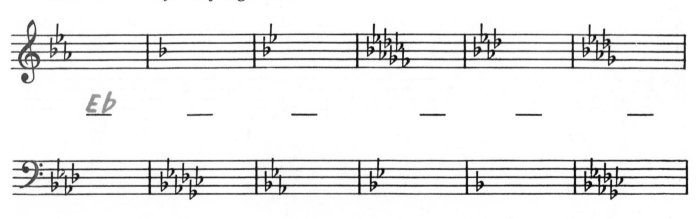

Eb

* With the exception of the Key of F, flat key signatures always have a <u>flat</u> in their names: B♭ (B-flat), E♭ (E-flat), etc.

TEACHER: Have the student drill on the flat key signatures using his BASTIEN "MUSIC FLASHCARDS."

Writing Major Flat Key Signatures

56. To write the Major flat key signatures:

> Write the flats in their order until you
> write one <u>more</u> flat than the key note.*

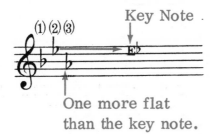

Write these Major key signatures.

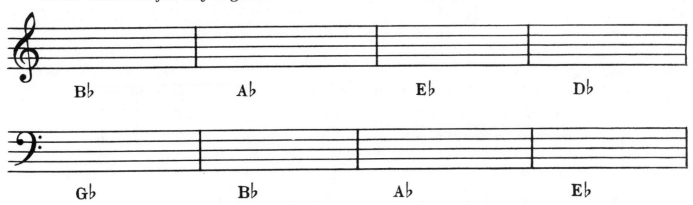

57. Write these Major key signatures in both clefs.

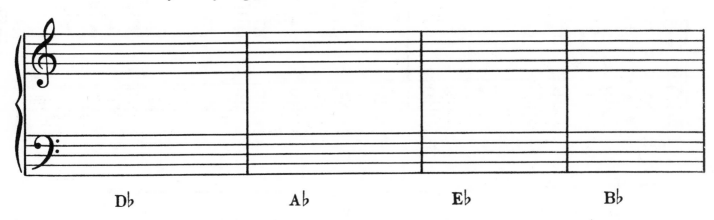

58. The order of flats is: B   E   A   D   G   C   F

The order of sharps is: F   C   G   D   A   E   B

How is the order of these letters related? _____

_____

*Exception: Key of F has only one flat.

Music Signs

59. This sign ₵ means ALLA BREVE (or "Cut Time"). There are <u>two</u> strong beats to the measure. The <u>alla breve</u> sign is usually used in place of 2/2 time.

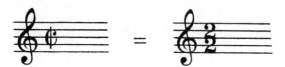

Draw <u>alla breve</u> signs on this Grand Staff.

60. These signs ⌐1.————⌐2.———— are ENDING SIGNS. These are <u>direction signs</u> that save space on the page for composers and printers.

Play this melody ("Long, Long Ago"). Follow the ending signs.

61. Complete the following sentences choosing words from the list below.

a. **ff** means *fortissimo* or *very loud*.

b. **p** means _____ or _____.

c. **mf** means _____ _____ or _____ _____.

d. **pp** means _____ or _____ _____.

e. **f** means _____ or _____ _____.

		very soft
pianissimo	soft	mezzo forte
forte	loud	medium loud
piano	very loud	fortissimo

WP 9

The Group 3 Keys (Db, Ab, Eb)

62. The GROUP 3 KEYS are Db, Ab, Eb. The pattern for the I chords in this group is "__black__ - white - __black__" keys. Play these chords.

Db Major
I Chord

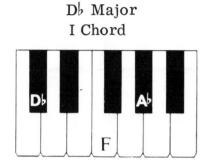

Ab Major
I Chord

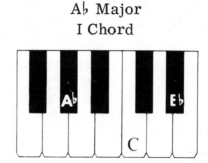

Eb Major
I Chord

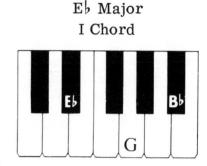

63. Draw these I chords on the staff. Add the necessary flats. Play these chords.

Db

Ab

Eb

64. The five finger positions of Db and Ab have only one white key. The five finger position of Eb has __two__ white keys. Play these five finger positions.

Db Major
Five Finger Position

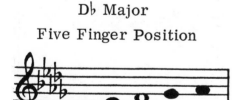

Ab Major
Five Finger Position

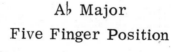

Eb Major
Five Finger Position

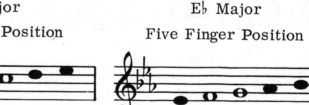

65. Draw the notes of these five finger positions on the staff. Add the necessary flats. Play these positions.

Db Major
Five Finger Position

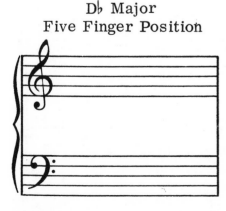

Ab Major
Five Finger Position

Eb Major
Five Finger Position

WP 9

Db Major Scale

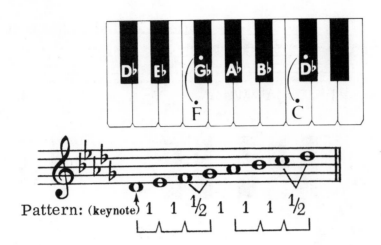

Pattern: (keynote) 1 1 ½ 1 1 1 ½

66. Draw the notes of the Db Major scale. Mark the half steps with a ∨ . Write in the fingering.* Play this scale with your R. H., then with your L. H.

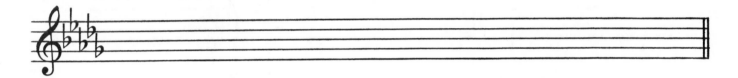

67. Write your own tempo markings and dynamics for these two scale pieces. Add your own title for each piece. Play both pieces. Watch the fingering.

TITLE: _____

TITLE: _____

* See "PIANO LESSONS, Level 3," page 46 for the Db Major scale fingering.

Primary Chords in D♭ Major

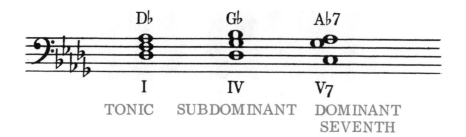

68. Draw the Primary Chords in D♭ Major. Use whole notes.

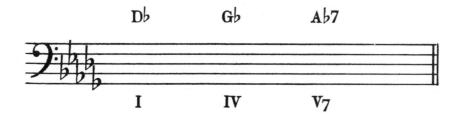

69. Draw the chords indicated. Add your own tempo markings and dynamics. Play this
    piece.

MICHAEL, ROW THE BOAT ASHORE

Traditional

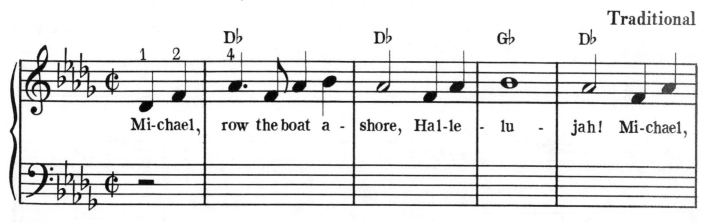

Experiment with these accompaniment styles. Play "Michael, Row the Boat Ashore"
again using either accompaniment style.

"Broken Chord" Bass   "Off-beat Chord" Bass

28

A♭ Major Scale

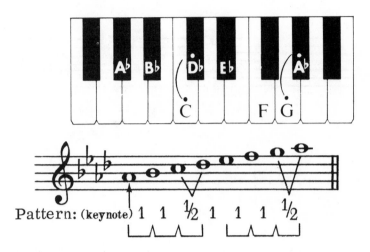

Pattern: (keynote) 1 1 ½ 1 1 1 ½

70. Draw the notes of the A♭ Major scale. Mark the half steps with a ∨ . Write in the fingering.* Play this scale with your R.H., then with your L.H.

71. Write your own tempo markings and dynamics for these two scale pieces. Add your own title for each piece. Play both pieces. Watch the fingering.

TITLE: _____

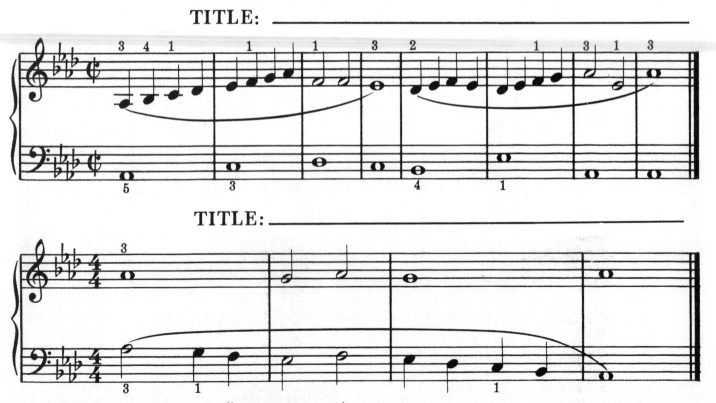

TITLE: _____

* See "PIANO LESSONS, Level 3," page 46 for the A♭ Major scale fingering.

WP 9

Primary Chords in A♭ Major

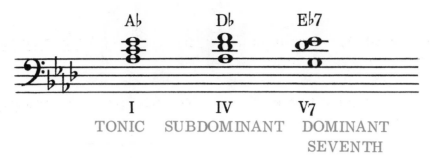

72. Draw the Primary Chords in A♭ Major. Use whole notes.

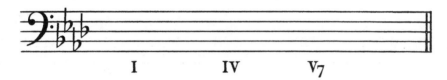

73. Draw the chords indicated. Add your own tempo markings and dynamics. Play this piece.

LOVE SOMEBODY   Traditional

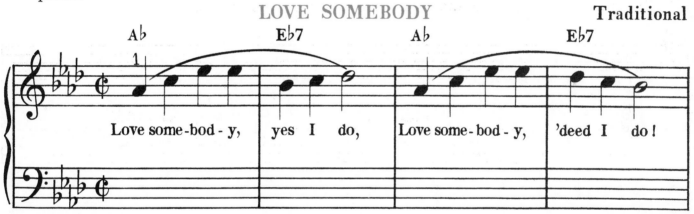

Love some-bod-y, yes I do, Love some-bod-y, 'deed I do!

Love some-bod-y, yes I do, Love some-bod-y but I won't say who!

Experiment with these accompaniment styles. Play "Love Somebody" again using either accompaniment style.

"Broken Chord" Bass   "Off-beat Chord" Bass

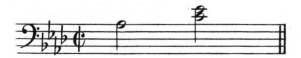

Eb Major Scale

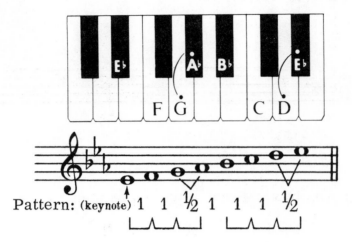

Pattern: (keynote) 1 1 ½ 1 1 1 ½

74. Draw the notes of the Eb Major scale. Mark the half steps with a ∨ . Write in the fingering.* Play this scale with your R.H., then with your L.H.

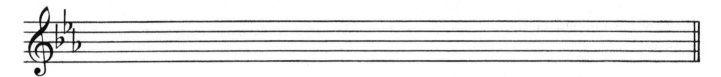

75. Write your own tempo markings and dynamics for these two scale pieces. Add your own title for each piece. Play both pieces. Watch the fingering.

TITLE: _____

TITLE: _____

*See "PIANO LESSONS, Level 3," page 46 for the Eb Major scale fingering.

Primary Chords in Eb Major

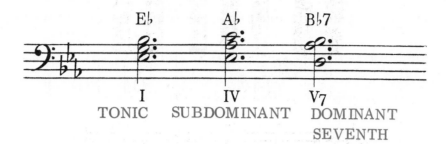

76. Draw the Primary Chords in Eb Major. Use dotted half notes.

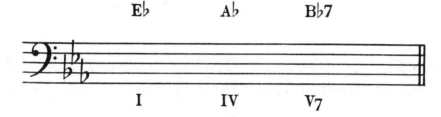

77. Draw the chords indicated. Add your own tempo markings and dynamics. Play this piece.

LULLABY

Johannes Brahms

Experiment with these accompaniment styles. Play "Lullaby" again using either accompaniment style.

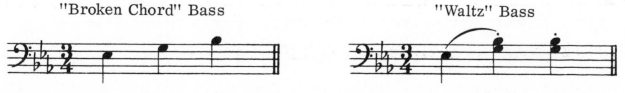

Circle of Keys

78. Study this chart showing the CIRCLE OF KEYS. The sharps are arranged from the top moving clockwise. The flats are arranged from the top moving counterclockwise.

There are fifteen Major keys -- seven sharp keys, seven flat keys, one with no sharps or flats. Likewise, there are fifteen Relative Minor keys. Each Major key has a relative minor key with the same key signature.

The keys at the bottom of the circle are called enharmonic. These keys have two names.

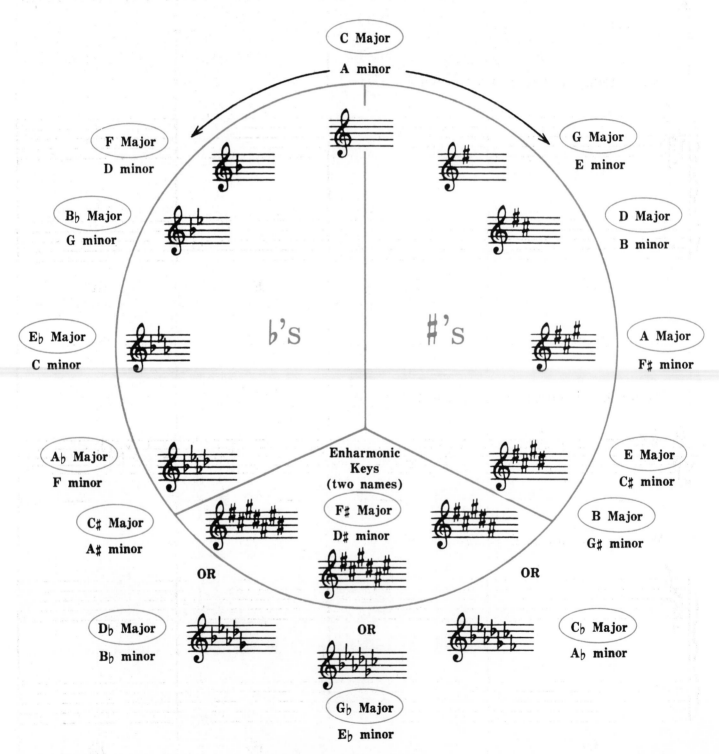

Key Signature Review

79. Write the order of sharps. *F#* __ __ __ __ __ __ __

80. Name these Major key signatures.

__ __ __ __ __ __

81. Write these Major key signatures.

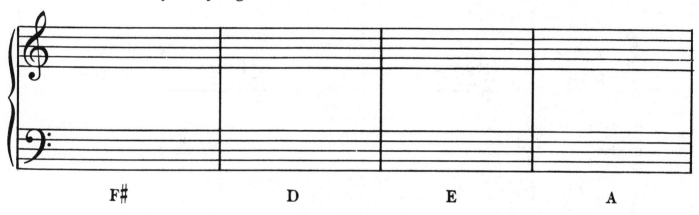

F#   D   E   A

82. Write the order of flats. *Bb* __ __ __ __ __ __ __

83. Name these Major key signatures.

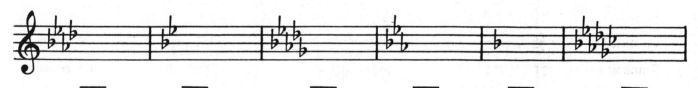

__ __ __ __ __ __

84. Write these Major key signatures.

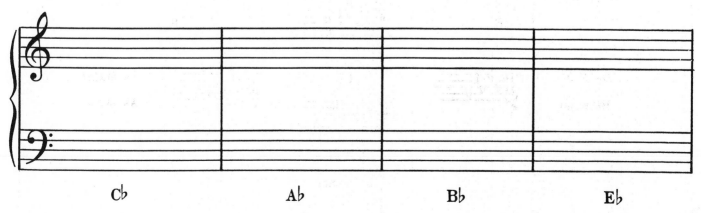

C♭   A♭   B♭   E♭

Leger Line and Space Note Review

85. Name these notes. The letter names spell words. Play them.

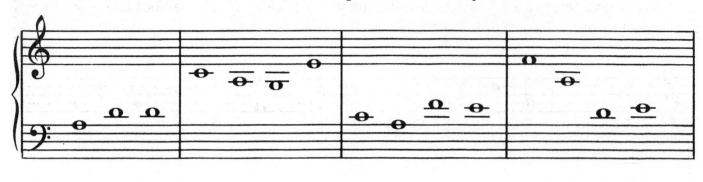

86. Name these notes. The letter names spell words. Play them.

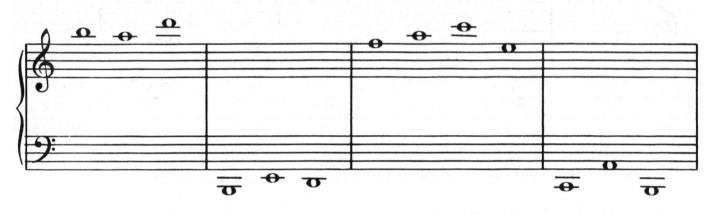

87. Draw each note two places on the staff. Make one of the notes a leger line or space note. Play these notes.

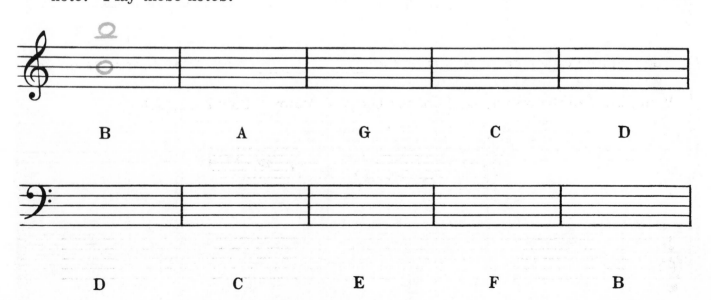

B   A   G   C   D

D   C   E   F   B

WP 9

FINAL REVIEW (Level 3)

1. Name these intervals of the scale. Write <u>M</u> for Major, <u>P</u> for Perfect and <u>2</u> for 2nd, <u>3</u> for 3rd, etc. Play these intervals.

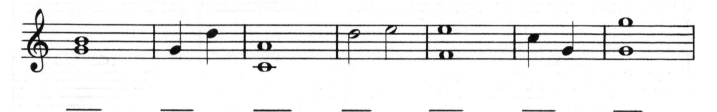

___ ___ ___ ___ ___ ___ ___

2. Draw an upper note to complete these intervals of the scale. Play these intervals.

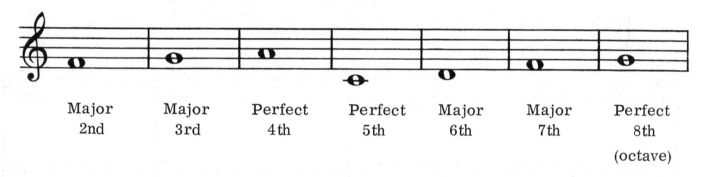

Major	Major	Perfect	Perfect	Major	Major	Perfect
2nd	3rd	4th	5th	6th	7th	8th
						(octave)

3. A triplet eighth note figure is equal to a _____ note.

Play and count this rhythm aloud.

4. The relative minor scale begins on the _____ tone of the Major scale.

Write the relative minor scale of the key of C Major. Play both scales.

5. Change this Natural Minor scale to a Harmonic Minor scale.   Play it.

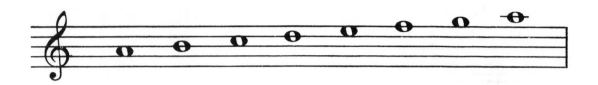

6. Change this Natural Minor scale to a Melodic Minor scale.   Play it.

7. To name the relative minor key signature, count down _____ half steps from the Major key name.

Write the Major key name and the relative minor key name for these signatures.

_____ Major   _____ minor   _____ Major   _____ minor

_____ Major   _____ minor   _____ Major   _____ minor

8. Name these Major and minor triads. Play them.

9. Write the inversions of this triad.

ROOT POSITION   FIRST INVERSION   SECOND INVERSION

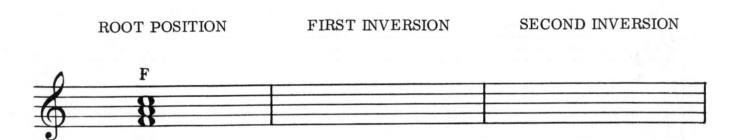

10. Circle the <u>root</u> of each chord. Write the root name of each chord. Play them.

11. Draw the Primary Chords in these keys. Play them.

F   Bb   C7   Eb   Ab   Bb7

I   IV   V7   I   IV   V7

WP 9

Manuscript Paper

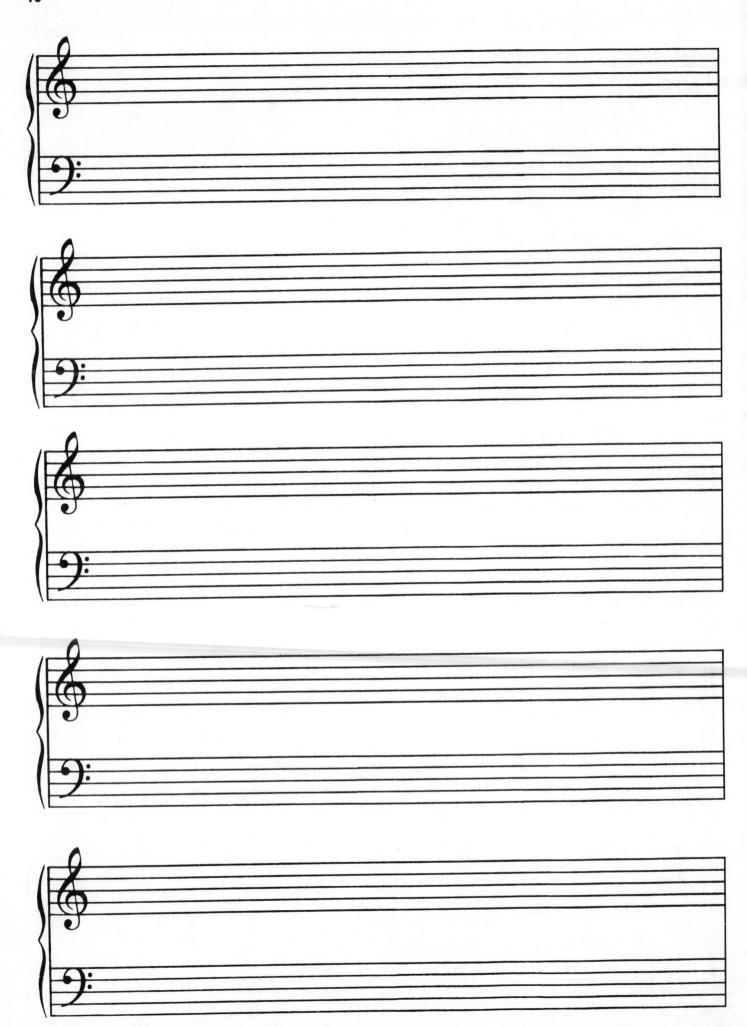